Share it!

Workbook

S Starter

Fiona Davis

macmillan
education

Table of Contents

1 Look and draw 🙂 or 🙁. 👀 ✏

2 Read the word. Then look and draw. ✏

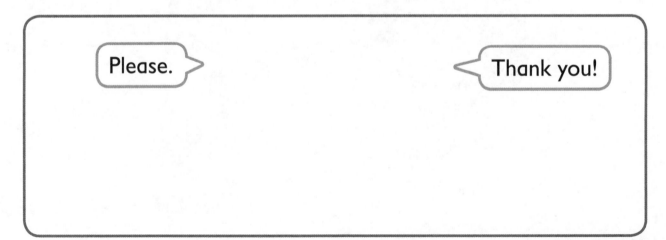

3 Look, read, and circle.

1

a Open your book.

(b) Close your book.

2

a Stand up.

b Sit down.

3

a Raise your hand.

b Listen.

4

a Open your book.

b Close your book.

5

a Raise your hand.

b Listen.

6

a Sit down.

b Stand up.

Alphabet

4 Look and match.

C   E   G   K

(g)   (c)   (k)   (e)

(z)   (t)   (m)   (r)

M   R   T   Z

5 Look and circle.

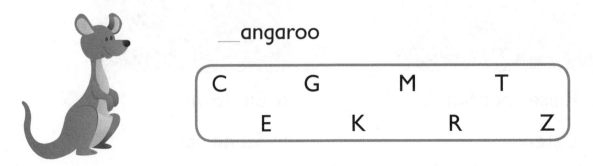

____ angaroo

C	G	M	T
E	K	R	Z

6 Look, draw lines, and color.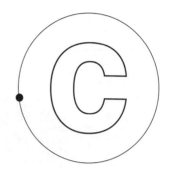

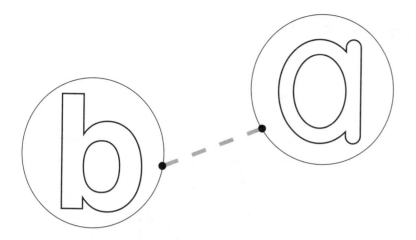

 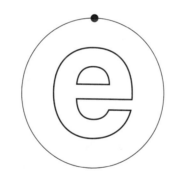 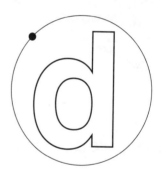

7 Look and write. Then color.

 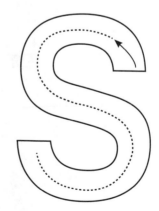

Lesson 1 Vocabulary

1 Look, read, and number.

1 ◁ Hi!   2 ◁ Bye!   3 ◁ Goodbye!   4 ◁ Hello!

2 Look, read, and circle.

1 ◁ Goodbye!   a    b

2 ◁ Hello!   a    b

Student Book page 10

1 Read and number. ☐3

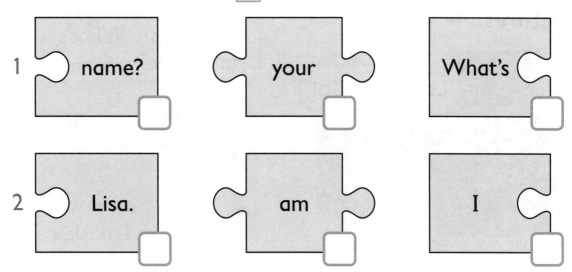

1 name?   your   What's

2 Lisa.   am   I

2 Look, read, and write. 👀 ✏️

1 ___'m Tom.

2 I'___ Tom.

1 Look and put the story in order. Number the pictures. 👀 ✏️ 3

a

Let's play! Go!

b

Hi, I'm Dan. What's your name?

I'm Alex.

c

Hello, I'm Nancy!

Nice to meet you. Let's play a game!

I'm Alex.

2 Look and circle. 👀 ✏️

1 Sit down.

2 Let's play.

3 Raise your hand.

1 Read, count, and match.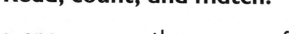

- one   - three   - five   - four   - two

- nine   - seven   - eight   - ten   - six

2 Draw lines. Then read the words.

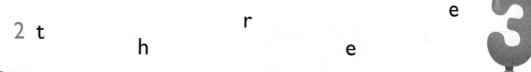

1 e   i   g   h   t

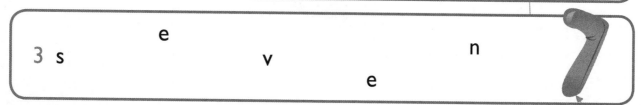

2 t   h   r   e   e

3 s   e   v   e   n

1 Read and match.

1 < Bye!

2 < How old are you?

3 < What's your name?

4 < Hello!

a I'm seven.

b Goodbye!

c Hi!

d I'm Sue.

2 Read and circle.

1 **What** / (**How**) old are you?

2 I'm **six** / **name**.

3 What's your **name** / **old**?

4 I'm **you** / **Sam**.

3 Write.

How old are you?

_____

1 Look, read, and number.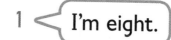

a

Hello. What's your name?

1 I'm eight.

b

How old are you?

2 Hi, I'm Lee.

c

Nice to meet you.

3 Nice to meet you, too.

2 Look, read, and match.

1 What's your name?   2 Hello!   3 How old are you?

a

b

c

Hi, Connor!

1 Look and draw your face.

2 Read and write.

Hello! I'm _____.

1 Write the letters.

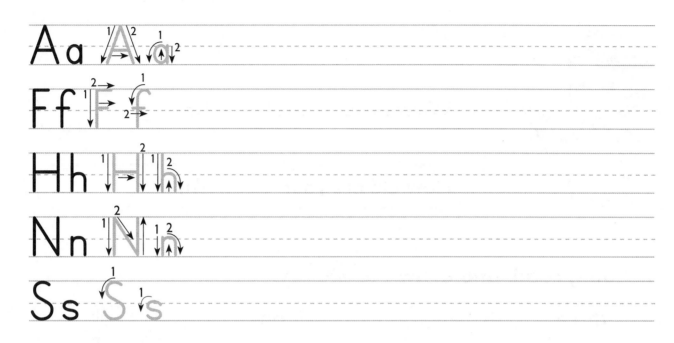

2 Complete the words. Then match.

1 f ive

2 ___ix

3 ___i!

4 ___nt

5 ___ine

a

b

c

d

e

Progress Tracker

1 Read and write.

1 Hi!

_____ !

2 What's your name?

I'm _____ .

3 How old are you?

I'm _____ .

2 Look, read, and draw.

1 three

2 one

3 four

4 two

3 Track it! Rate your progress in Unit 1.

Can you say *hello* and count to ten?

Lesson 1 Vocabulary

1 Look, read, and check (✔).

1   a pen ✔
   b crayon ☐

2   a eraser ☐
   b ruler ☐

3   a book ☐
   b ruler ☐

4  a pencil ☐
   b pen ☐

5  a book ☐
   b pencil case ☐

6   a crayon ☐
   b pencil ☐

2 Look, read, and match.

1 e   ___rayon

2 p   ___encil

3 c   ___raser

4 b   ___uler

5 r   ___ook

Lesson 2 Grammar

1 Look, read, and circle.

1

It's **a** / **an** pencil.

2

It's **a** / **an** desk.

3

It's **a** / **an** eraser.

4

It's **a** / **an** pencil case.

2 Look and write.

1 It is = It _____

2 What is = What _____

3 I am = I __m

1 Look, read, and number.

1 It's a face!

a

2 It's a red and blue pen!

b

3 It's a mouse!

c

2 Look and circle.

1 Stand up.

2 Close your book.

3 Share ideas.

Lesson 4 Vocabulary

1 Look, find, and write check (✔) or cross (✗).

1 book ☐   2 chair ☐   3 computer ☐

4 crayon ☐   5 desk ☐   6 door ☐

7 pen ☐   8 pencil ☐   9 pencil case ☐

10 ruler ☐   11 window ☐   12 eraser ☐

1 Look, count, and write.

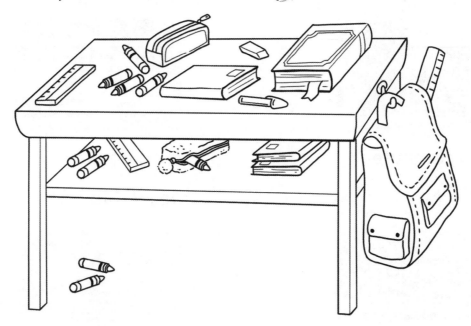

How many ...

1 pencil cases? [2] 2 books? [ ] 3 rulers? [ ]

4 crayons? [ ] 5 desks? [ ] 6 erasers? [ ]

2 Make two questions. Draw lines and color.

(What's)——(this?)

(pencils?)

(How)

(many)

(old)

(you?)

(How) (are)

Lesson 6 Art CLIL

1 Look, read, and circle *Yes* or *No*.

1

It's a computer.

Yes / No

2

It's a book.

Yes / No

3

It's a ruler.

Yes / No

4

It's a pencil case.

Yes / No

2 Read and draw.

1 It's a pen.

2 It's a window.

1 Look, read, and number.

1 It's an eraser.   2 It's a chair.   3 It's a door.
4 It's a pencil case.

a

b

c

d

2 Look and circle.

1 door

2 desk

3 chair

1 Write the letters.

C c C c

D d D d

E e E e

P p P p

W w W w

2 Complete the words. Then match.

1 ___omputer

2 ___hale

3 ___lephant

4 ___en

5 ___oor

a

b

c

d

e

Student Book page 28

1 Draw, read, and circle.

1

2

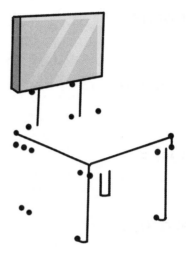

What's this?
It's a **pencil** / **pen**.

What's this?
It's a **desk** / **chair**.

2 Read and match.

1 What's this?

2 How old are you?

3 What's your name?

4 How many books?

a Five.

b It's a computer.

c I'm Mark.

d I'm six.

3 Track it! Rate your progress in Unit 2.

Can you talk about things in your classroom?

1 Look, read, and match.

1 teacher

2 window

3 desks

4 erasers

5 crayons

6 pencils

a

b

c

d

e

f

2 Look, find, and circle.

Circle:

the window

the chairs

the computer

the ruler

the clock

the teacher

3 Look, count, and write.

How many ...

1 teachers? ☐   2 chairs? ☐   3 rulers? ☐

4 computers? ☐   5 pencil cases? ☐   6 clocks? ☐

4 Share Your World Draw and color.

My Classroom

Lesson 1 Vocabulary

1 Look, read, and color. 👀

> 1 = pink   2 = brown   3 = red   4 = green
> 5 = purple   6 = orange   7 = blue   8 = yellow

2 Read and color.

1 red

2 blue

1 Read and color.

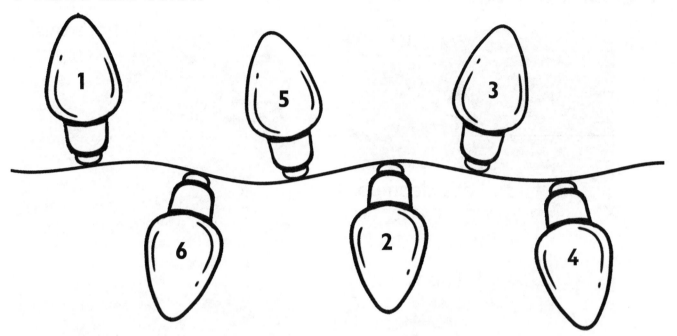

Key

1 It's yellow.   2 It's green.   3 It's pink.

4 It's purple.   5 It's blue.   6 It's orange.

2 Read, color, and write. ✏️

1

2

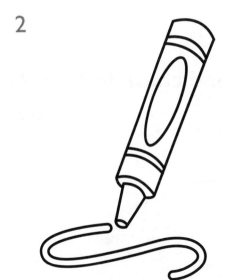

It ___ red.   ___ ___'s brown.

1 Look, read, and number.  3

OK!

Let's clean up.

What's this?

This is fun!

Oh, no!
Come back!

Be careful,
May!

2 Look and check (✔).

Be careful!

1

2

1 Look and match.

circle   heart   star

square   rectangle   triangle

2 Look, read, and color.

1 A red square

2 A purple triangle

3 An orange star

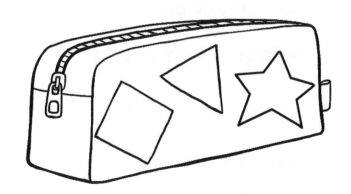

Lesson 5 Grammar

1 Look, draw, and circle.

1

Is it a square?

(Yes, it is.) / No, it isn't.

2

Is it a triangle?

Yes, it is. / No, it isn't.

3

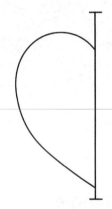

Is it a star?

Yes, it is. / No, it isn't.

4

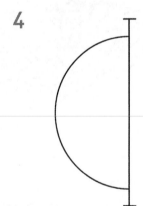

Is it a circle?

Yes, it is. / No, it isn't.

2 Read and circle.

1 **What** / **Is** it a heart?

2 **How** / **Is** it yellow?

3 **What's** / **Is** this?

4 **Is** / **How** it a rectangle?

Student Book page 39

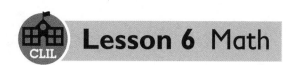

1 Read and draw.

circle  square  triangle  heart

2 Read, number, and draw. ☐3

1 A heart, a rectangle, a star, and a triangle.

2 A heart, a rectangle, a triangle, and a circle.

3 Two stars, a circle, and a heart.

4 Two stars, a heart, and a square.

a ☐2

b ☐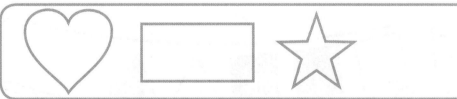

c ☐

d ☐

Lesson 7 Project

1 Look and draw. What's next?

2 Look at Activity 1 and count.

1 How many circles? ☐

2 How many stars? ☐

3 How many hearts? ☐

1 Write the letters.

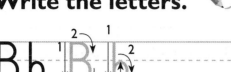

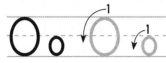

2 Complete the words. Then match.

1 ___lack

2 ___strich

3 ___uler

4 ___tar

5 ___ctopus

6 ___quare

a

b

c

d

e

f

Progress Tracker

1 Read, number, and color.

> 1 It's a circle. It's yellow.   2 It's a heart. It's pink.
>
> 3 It's a star. It's blue.   4 It's a rectangle. It's purple.
>
> 5 It's a triangle. It's red.   6 It's a square. It's brown.

a

b

c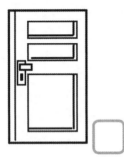

d

e

f

2 Track it! Rate your progress in Unit 3.

Can you talk about colors and shapes?

Lesson 1 Vocabulary

1 Look, read, and number. 👁👁 ✏️ 3

a grandma ☐   b mom ☐   c sister ☐

d grandpa ☐   e dad ☐   f brother ☐

2 Find five words. Look and color. 👁👁

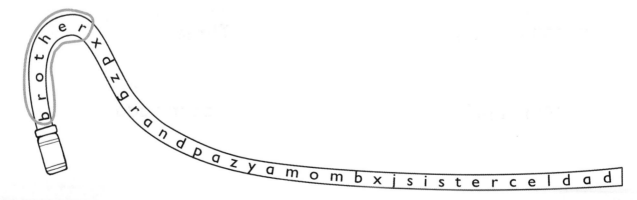

Lesson 2 Grammar

1 Read and number. 3

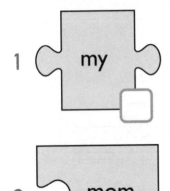 1 my

 He's

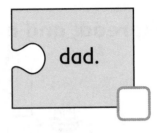 dad.

 2 mom.

 my

 She's

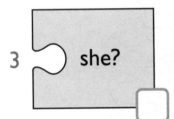 3 she?

 Who

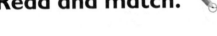 is

2 Read and match.

1 How many books?

2 Who's she?

3 What's this?

4 Who's he?

a She's my grandma.

b It's a computer.

c Three.

d He's my dad.

Student Book page 45

1 Look and match.

1 Who's she, Nancy?

2 My mom and my sister.

3 Bye!

a

Who's this, Alex?

b

Bye, Dan!

c

She's my grandma.

2 Look and check (✔).

Be patient!

1

2

Lesson 4 Vocabulary

1 Look, read, and circle. 👀 ✏️

1

kitchen / dining room

2

bedroom / living room

3

kitchen / bathroom

4

dining room / bathroom

5

living room / bedroom

2 Look and color. 👀

living room = orange   bathroom = blue

a

b

c

d

e
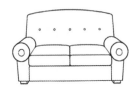

f
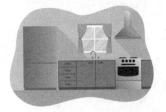

Student Book page 48

1 Look, read, and circle.

1 Where's Grandpa? **He's / She's** in the dining room.

2 Where's my sister? **He's / She's** in the bedroom.

3 Where's Mom? **He's / She's** in the living room.

2 Look at Activity 1. Then read and write check (✔) or cross (✗).

1 I'm in the dining room.

2 My sister is in the bedroom.

3 My grandma is in the living room.

4 My brother is in the kitchen.

5 My grandpa is in the dining room.

Lesson 6 Social Studies

1 Look, read, and number. 👀 ✏️ 3

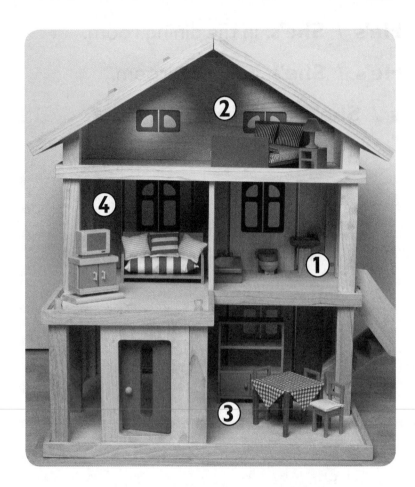

a living room ☐

b bedroom ☐

c kitchen ☐

d bathroom ☐

2 Look at Activity 1. Read and circle *Yes* or *No*. 👀 ✏️

1 How many kitchens? One.   Yes / No

2 How many bathrooms? Two.   Yes / No

3 How many living rooms? One.   Yes / No

4 How many dining rooms? One.   Yes / No

5 How many bedrooms? Four.   Yes / No

Student Book page 50

1 Look, read, and match. 👁👁 ✏

1 Where's Mom?

She's in the bathroom.

2 Where's Juan?

He's in the bedroom.

3 Who's he?

He's my dad. He's in the living room.

4 Who's she?

She's my grandma. She's in the kitchen.

2 Look, circle, and draw. 👁👁 ✏ 👤

She's my **sister** / **mom** / **grandma**.

1 Write the letters.

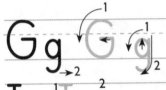

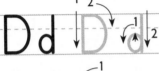

2 Complete the words. Then match.

1 ___ad

a

2 ___guana

b

3 ___randma

c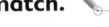

4 ___esk

d

5 ___randpa

e

6 ___gloo

f

1 Look, read, and number.

> 1 = Who?   2 = Where?

a

b

c

d

2 Look, read, and circle. 👀✏️

1

Grandpa / Grandma is in the **living room / dining room**.

2

Mom / Dad is in the **bedroom / kitchen**.

3 Track it! Rate your progress in Unit 4.

Can you talk about your family and home?

1 Look, read, and number.

> 1 semi-circle   2 circle   3 rectangle   4 triangle

a ☐

b ☐

c ☐

d ☐

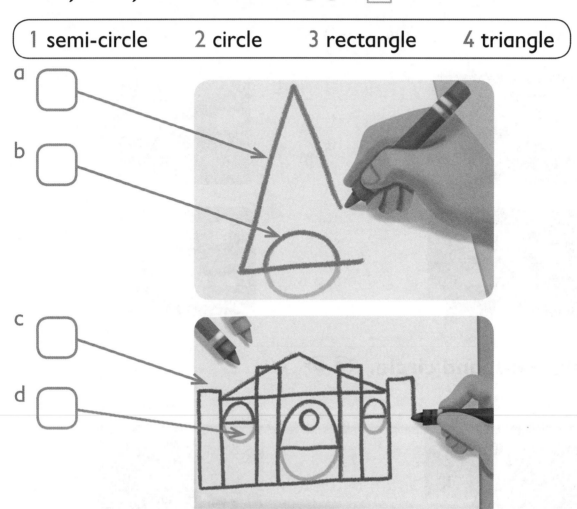

2 Look, read, and color. 👀

> square = blue
> rectangle = yellow
> triangle = purple
> circle = pink
> semi-circle = green

3 Look and draw. 👀✏️🧍

Draw a star with a pencil ✏️ and a ruler ▬.

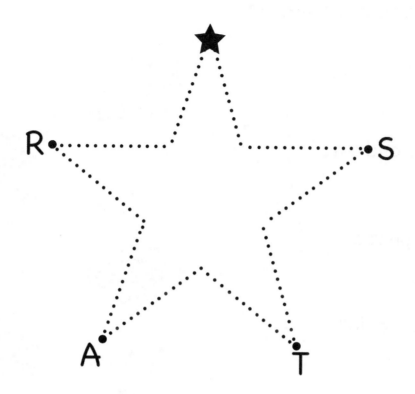

4 Share Your World Draw and color. ✏️🧍

My Shape Drawing

5 My Toys

Lesson 1 Vocabulary

1 Look, read, and number.

a a ball and a car ☐

b a teddy bear and a doll ☐

c a ball and a puzzle ☐

d a scooter and a doll ☐

e a scooter and a car ☐

1

2

3

4

5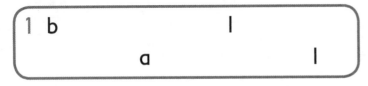

2 Draw lines. Then match.

1 b   l
     a   l

2 s   o   t   r
   c   o   e

3 d   l
   o   l

a

b

c

Student Book page 58

1 Look, read, and circle. 👀 ✏️

1 I **have** / **don't have** a book.

2 I **have** / **don't have** a scooter.

4 I **have** / **don't have** a doll.

3 I **have** / **don't have** a teddy bear.

2 Look and read. Color the words to complete the sentence. 👀

I	red	have	a	star.
am	don't	yes	six	car.

1 Look, read, and number.

1 Put the ball here, Jake!

2 And I have pens.

3 Look! I have a yellow car.

a

> Great! Put the car here, please.

b

> Put the pens here, May.

c

2 Look and check (✔).

Clean up!

1

2

1 Look and draw. Then number.

1 bike 2 kite 3 skateboard 4 robot
5 yo-yo 6 video game

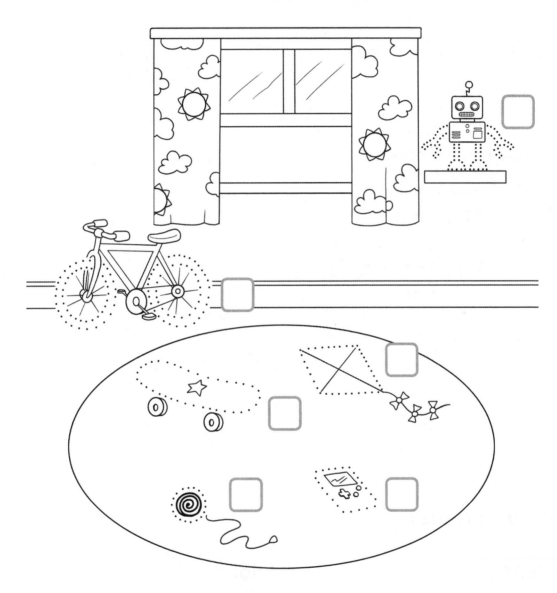

2 Write. Then look at Activity 1 and color.

a a red __ideo game

b a blue __obot

c a purple __ike

d a pink __kateboard

Lesson 5 Grammar

1 Look, read, and circle.

1 Do you have a kite?

Yes, I do. / No, I don't.

2 Do you have a robot?

Yes, I do. / No, I don't.

3 Do you have a yo-yo?

Yes, I do. / No, I don't.

2 Read and match.

1 I don't   a I don't.

2 Do you   b have a video game.

3 Yes,   c have a bike?

4 No,   d I do.

1 Complete the words. Then match.

1 It's an ___ctopus.

a

2 It's a ___ar.

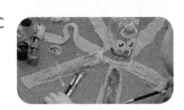
b

3 It's a ___at.

c

2 Look and circle the plastic.

1

2

3

4

5

1 Look and count. How many paper plates?

2 Look and color. Then match.

| 1 = blue | 2 = yellow | 3 = red | 4 = brown |

a · I have a red and yellow car.

b · I have a blue and brown car.

1 Write the letters.

K k
T t
U u
V v

2 Complete the words. Then match.

1 ___ideo game

2 ___ite

3 ___mbrella

4 ___oys

5 ___iolin

6 ___nder

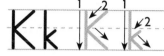
a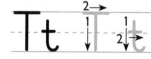

b

c

d

e

f

1 Find the toys.

videogameorangedollteddybearheartkiteskateboardpuzzle

2 Who says this? Look, read, and number. 👀 ✏️3️⃣

| 1 = Ed | 2 = Dee | 3 = Ed and Dee |

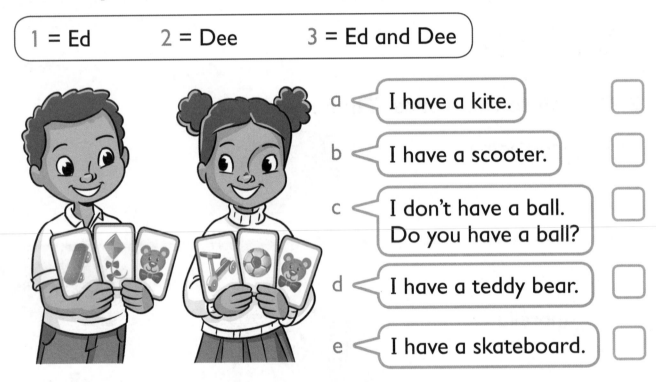

a — I have a kite. ☐

b — I have a scooter. ☐

c — I don't have a ball. Do you have a ball? ☐

d — I have a teddy bear. ☐

e — I have a skateboard. ☐

3 Track it! Rate your progress in Unit 5.

Can you talk about toys?

Student Book page 67

Lesson 1 Vocabulary

1 Look, read, and check (✔).

1  fish ☐
turtle ☐

2  dog ☐
fish ☐

3  bird ☐
cat ☐

4  rabbit ☐
bird ☐

5  rabbit ☐
dog ☐

6 turtle ☐
cat ☐

2 Which is different? Read and circle.

1   a cat   b dog   c (ball)

2   a bird   b desk   c rabbit

3   a star   b turtle   c square

4   a bird   b fish   c kite

Lesson 2 Grammar

1 Look, read, and number.

> 1 = it   2 = they

a

b

c

d

2 Look, read, and circle.

1

It's / They're birds.

2

It's / They're a dog.

3

It's / They're turtles.

Student Book page 69

1 Look, read, and circle.

They're really small.

Wow! Look, May! They're turtles.

Here are the fish. They're small, too.

Oh, they're orange.

Wow! They're so cool!

Look, May! They're starfish.

1 The turtles are **small** / **big** / **orange**.

2 The fish are **small and orange** / **big and blue** / **small and pink**.

3 The starfish are **green** / **cool** / **squares**.

2 Look and check (✔).

Pay attention!

1

2

Lesson 4 Vocabulary

1 Look, read, and number. 👀✏️ 3

> 1 lion   2 zebra   3 snake   4 monkey
> 5 giraffe   6 elephant

Which animal is in the box? ☐

2 Look, read, and circle. 👀✏️

How many animals? four / five / six

1 Look, read, and circle.

1 Are they elephants?

Yes, they are. / No, they aren't.

2 Are they lions?

Yes, they are. / No, they aren't.

3 Are they monkeys?

Yes, they are. / No, they aren't.

4 Are they zebras?

Yes, they are. / No, they aren't.

2 Look, read, and circle.

1  Are they **monkeys** / **elephants**?
Yes, they are.

2  What **are they** / **is it**?
They're zebras.

3  Are they **snakes** / **elephants**?
No, they aren't.

Lesson 6 Science CLIL

1 Look, read, and number. 👀 ✏️ 3

1

2

3

4

a I see two. ☐

c They're in the tree.

☐ and ☐

b I see three. ☐

d They're big animals.

☐ and ☐

2 Draw lines. Then read the words.

1 b   i   s
                    d
            r

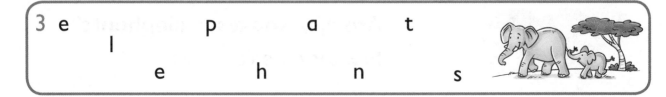

2 w   a   e
                             s
       h   l

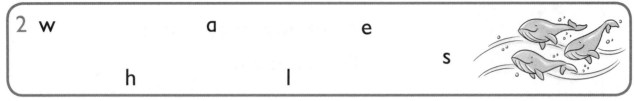

3 e   p   a   t
      l
        e   h   n   s

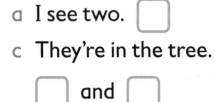

1 Look, read, and check (✔).

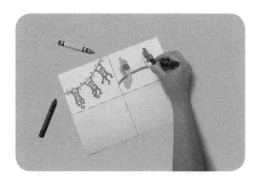

1 They're monkeys and rabbits. ☐

2 They're cats and birds. ☐

3 They're birds and monkeys. ☐

4 They're snakes and monkeys. ☐

2 Look, read, and write check (✔) or cross (✗).

1

Are they birds?
Yes, they are. ☐
No, they aren't. ☐

2

Are they turtles?
Yes, they are. ☐
No, they aren't. ☐

3

Are they dogs?
Yes, they are. ☐
No, they aren't. ☐

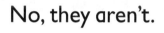

1 Write the letters.

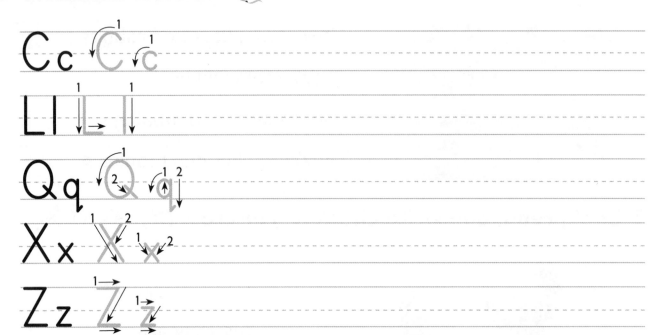

2 Complete the words. Then match.

1 ___ion

2 ___uail

3 ___ebra

4 ___at

5 ___-ray fish

6 ___izard

a

b

c

d

e

f

Student Book page 76

1 Look, read, and check (✔). 👀

1 fish ☐	2 snake ☐	3 cat ☐
4 giraffe ☐	5 zebra ☐	6 lion ☐
7 bird ☐	8 monkey ☐	9 turtle ☐

2 Draw, read, and circle. ✏️

1 Are they elephants?

Yes, they are. / No, they aren't.

2 What are they?

They **are** / **aren't** rabbits.

3 Track it! Rate your progress in Unit 6.

Can you talk about animals?

1 Look, read, and number. 👀 ✏️ 3

1 I have a dog.
   It's black.

a

2 I have a teddy bear.
   It's small and cute.

b

3 I have a rabbit.
   It's gray and brown.

c

4 I have a bird.
   It's small and yellow.

d

2 Look at Activity 1. Read and color the animals. 👀

What color is the teddy bear?

It's _____.

3 Look and match. 👁️👁️ ✏️

1 Arctic foxes

2 snowy owls

3 polar bears

4 Arctic hares

4 Share Your World Draw and color. ✏️🧍

My Favorite Arctic Animal

Lesson 1 Vocabulary

1 Look, read, and match. 👀 ✏️

1 milk   2 ice cream   3 cake

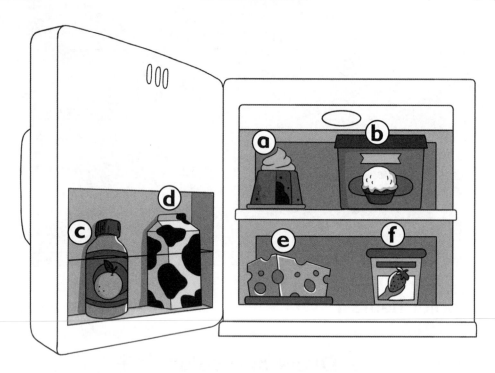

4 orange juice   5 yogurt   6 cheese

2 Look, find, and circle. 👀 ✏️

A	C	M	I	L	K	U	B
M	N	Y	O	G	U	R	T
C	A	K	E	I	E	C	R
E	C	H	E	E	S	E	K

1    2   3    4

Student Book page 82

1 Read and draw  or .

1 ☺ I like orange juice.

2 ◯ I like ice cream.

3 ◯ I don't like cheese.

4 ◯ I like yogurt.

5 ◯ I don't like cake.

6 ◯ I don't like milk.

2 Look, read, and number. 3

1 I like orange juice.

2 I don't like cake.

☐ ☐   ☐ ☐

3 I don't like orange juice.

4 I like cake.

1 Look, read, and number. 👀 ✏️ 3

> 1 Yes, I do!   2 No … I love it!
> 3 Yes, but I don't like it in my ice cream.

a

But you like yogurt, May.

b Do you like orange juice?

c Do you like it, May?

2 Look, read, and circle. 👀 ✏️

Try something **blue** / **who** / **new** !

1 Look, read, and write.

1
___oup

2
___alad

3
___ish

4
___ice

5
___izza

6
___read

2 Look, read, and check (✔).

1	bread	☐
2	soup	☐
3	rice	☐
4	salad	☐
5	pizza	☐
6	yogurt	☐
7	cheese	☐
8	milk	☐
9	fish	☐

Lesson 5 Grammar

1 Look, read, and circle.

1 Do you like salad?

Yes, I do. /
No, I don't.

2 Do you like fish?

Yes, I do. /
No, I don't.

3 **Do you / Are you** like pizza?

Yes, I do

2 Look and read. Color the words to make sentences.

1

Do	you	yes	milk?
Please	two	like	milk.

2

But	I	do.
No,	like	don't.

1 Look, read, and write.

cake   milk   rice   salad   yogurt

1 I like [milk] m___l___.

2 I like fish and [rice] r___c___.

3 I like [cake] c___k___.

4 I don't like [salad] ___a___a___.

5 I like [yogurt] y___g___r___.

2 Read and match.

1 I drink milk   a fish and rice for lunch.

2 I eat   b on my birthday.

3 I eat cake   c at home.

Lesson 7 Project

1 Read and draw lines.

bread

cake

cheese

milk

orange juice

salad

I eat …

I drink …

2 Read and circle for you.

1 I drink **milk** / **orange juice** at home.

2 I eat **pizza** / **rice** / **cheese** at school.

3 I like **salad** / **yogurt** / **cake**.

4 I don't like **ice cream** / **fish**.

Student Book page 89

1 Write the letters. ✏️

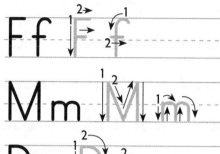

F f F f

M m M m

P p P p

Y y Y y

2 Complete the words. Then match. ✏️

1 __izza

2 __ish

3 __o-yo

4 __onkey

5 __ood

6 __uzzle

a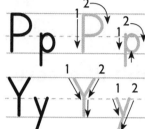

b

c

d

e

f

Progress Tracker

1 Look, read, and circle.

1 I **like** / **don't like** milk.

2 I **like** / **don't like** cheese.

3 I **like** / **don't like** bread.

4 I **like** / **don't like** salad.

5 I **like** / **don't like** cake.

2 Read and color to make sentences.

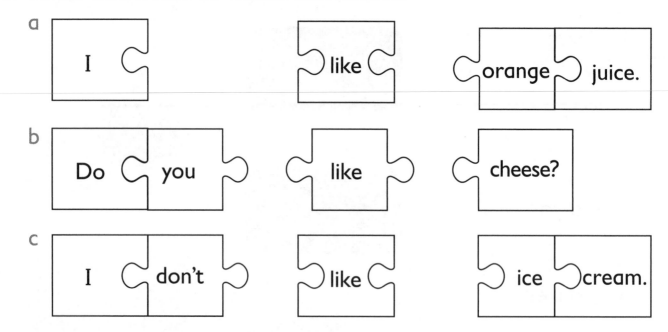

a   I   like   orange   juice.

b   Do   you   like   cheese?

c   I   don't   like   ice   cream.

3 Track it! Rate your progress in Unit 7.

Can you talk about food you like?

Lesson 1 Vocabulary

1 Look, read, and number. 👁️👁️ ✏️ 3

> 1 talk and read   2 run and walk
> 3 catch and throw   4 read and run

a

b

c

d

2 Which is different? Read and circle. ✏️

1 a turtle   b run   c fish

2 a read   b throw   c rice

3 a zebra   b walk   c talk

4 a desk   b pen   c catch

Lesson 2 Grammar

2 Look, read, and write check (✔) or cross (✘).

1 I can throw. ☐

2 I can catch. ☐

3 I can run. ☐

2 Look, read, and write.

1 It ___ an walk.

2 It ca___ run.

3 It ___ ___ ___ jump!

1 Look, read, and circle.

1 I like to run!

May / Alex

2 I don't like to read.

Alex / May

3 I like this book.

May / Alex

4 You're a good friend.

Alex / May / Alex and May

2 Draw lines. Then read and circle.

Be   good

  a   friend.

a

b

Lesson 4 Vocabulary

1 Look, read, and circle.

1

sing / jump

2

draw / dance

3

sing / paint

4

paint / clap

5

jump / dance

6

clap / draw

2 Read and write.

(d   k   p   ~~r~~)

1

r	e	a	d

r	u	n

2

	a	n	c	e

	r	a	w

3

j	u	m	

c	l	a	

4

t	a	l	

w	a	l	

1 Color to make a question and two answers.

Can

No, I

can't.

you paint?

can.

Yes,

I

2 Look, read, and write *Yes* or *No*.

1 Can you jump?

_____ , I can.

2 Can you sing?

_____ , I can't.

3 Can you paint?

_____ , I can.

1 Look, read, and match.

1

Dance Club

Sports Club

2

3

Story Club

Art Club

4

2 Look, read, and number. 3

1 Singing and Dance Club

2 Sports Club

3 Story Club

4 Art Club

a I can read and talk about a book. ☐

b I can catch and throw. ☐

c I can draw and paint. ☐

d I can sing and dance. ☐

1 Draw a friend. Then write their name and circle.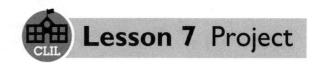

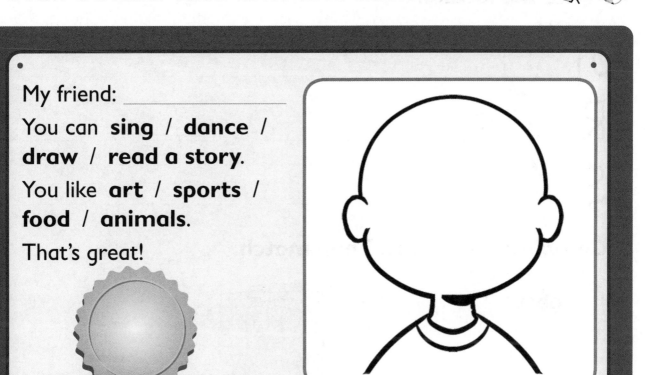

My friend: _____

You can **sing** / **dance** / **draw** / **read a story**.

You like **art** / **sports** / **food** / **animals**.

That's great!

2 Read, write, and circle.

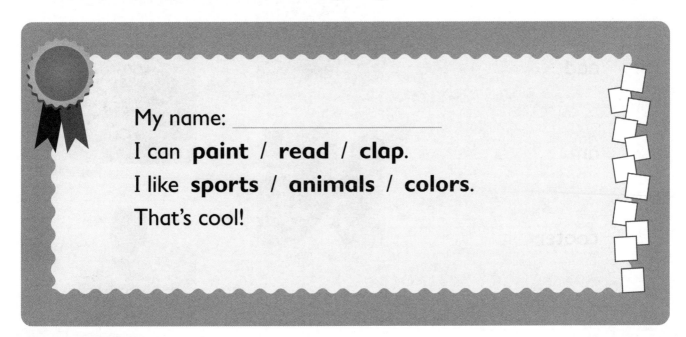

My name: _____

I can **paint** / **read** / **clap**.

I like **sports** / **animals** / **colors**.

That's cool!

1 Write the letters.

Jj Jj
Rr Rr
Ss Ss

2 Complete the words. Then match.

1 __obot

2 __ing

3 __ar

4 __ead

5 __am

6 __cooter

a

b
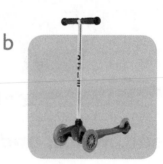

c

d

e

f

Student Book page 100

1 Look, read, and number. 👀✏️ 3

a Can you talk? ☐   b How old are you? ☐

c Do you like cake? ☐   d What's your name? ☐

1 I'm Rob the robot. Nice to meet you!

2 No, I don't.

4 I'm three.

3 Yes, I can.

2 Look, read, and circle. 👀✏️

1 I **can / can't** run.
2 I **can / can't** jump.
3 I **can / can't** dance.

3 Track it! Rate your progress in Unit 8.

Can you talk about actions?

1 Look, read, and match.

1

a crocodile

2

b party

3

c mouse-deer

4

d king

2 Look, read, and number. 3

1 jump   2 party   3 eat   4 fruit

a

I like ☐.
I can ☐.

b

You're small.
I can ☐ you!

c

"A ☐" Yes, please!

3 Look, read, and write. Who says this?

M = mouse-deer   C = crocodile

1 "I like fruit." M

2 "I can eat you!" ___

3 "A party! Yes, please!" ___

4 "I can jump!" ___

5 "Goodbye crocodiles!" ___

6 "Grrrrraaaaah!" ___

4 Share Your World Draw and color.

My Favorite Animal in the Story

Word Work Unit 1

1 Look and write. 👀 ✏️

2 Look and write check (✔) or cross (✗). 👀 ✏️

1

2

one	☐		six	☐
two	☐		seven	☐
three	☐		eight	☐
four	☐		nine	☐
five	☐		ten	☐

Student Book pages 10 and 14

1 Look and write.

1 crayon

2 eraser

3 pencil

4 desk

5 chair

2 Look and circle. Then draw.

1
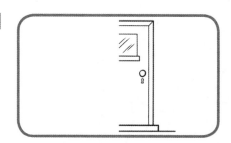
pen / door

2
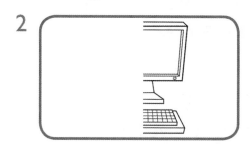
computer / window

3
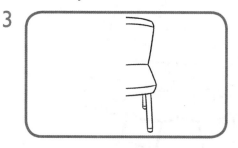
chair / pencil case

4
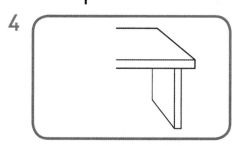
book / desk

1 Look, draw, and write.

1 rectangle

2 square

3 heart

4 circle

2 Read and color.

circle = blue

square = green

heart = red

star = pink

rectangle = yellow

triangle = orange

1 Look and write.

me

1 dad   2 sister   3 brother   4 grandma

2 Look and circle.

1

kitchen / living room

2

dining room / bathroom

3

bedroom / kitchen

4

bathroom / living room

1 Look and write. Then number.

a **b**all ☐

b **c**ar ☐

c **v**ideo game ☐

d **r**obot ☐

e **s**kateboard ☐

f **t**eddy bear ☐

g **k**ite ☐

h **d**oll ☐

2 Look and write check (✔) or cross (✗).

1

bike ☐

scooter ☐

car ☐

robot ☐

skateboard ☐

2

doll ☐

ball ☐

robot ☐

yo-yo ☐

teddy bear ☐

1 Look and write. 👀 ✏️

1

Cat

2

lion

3

Zebra

4

bird

2 Read and draw. ✏️ 🧍

1

an orange fish

2

a yellow giraffe

3

a brown rabbit

4

a green snake

5

a gray elephant

1 Look and write.

I like 1 yogurt and 2 pizza!

I don't like 3 milk or 4 fish.

2 Read and color.

soup = yellow   cake = brown

salad = red and green   ice cream = pink

rice = purple   cheese = orange

1 Look and write. Then match.

Sing   Clap   run

jump   dance   throw

2 Look and circle.

1

dance / walk / throw

2

talk / paint / run

3

catch / draw / read

4

sing / clap / jump

Macmillan Education Limited
4 Crinan Street
London N1 9XW

Companies and representatives throughout the world

Share It! Starter Workbook ISBN 978-1-380-02265-3

Share It! Starter Workbook and Digital Workbook ISBN 978-1-380-06938-2

Text, design and illustration Macmillan Education Limited 2021
Written by Fiona Davis

Original design by Pronk Media, Inc.
Page make-up by SPi Technologies, Inc.
Illustrated by Denis Alonso (Beehive Illustration) pp. 4, 6, 7, 8, 9, 11, 20, 21, 28, 29, 31, 32, 37, 40, 41, 46, 47, 48, 49, 51, 52, 58, 60, 61, 68, 69, 71, 77, 78, 81; Henrique Brum (Beehive Illustration) pp. 13, 14, 16, 23, 25, 34, 36, 53, 54, 56, 62, 63, 65, 73, 74, 76, 83, 85; Laura Estrada Ferraz (Beehive Illustration) pp. 66; Michelle Simpson (Advocate Art) pp. 27; Matt Ward (Beehive Illustration) pp. 30, 39, 50, 59, 88–95.

Cover design by Roberto Martinez, Marcin Rojek, and Wojciech Szulik

Cover illustration Emi Ordás
Cover photograph by Getty Images/iStock/Pollyana Ventura, Getty Images/Hero Images

Picture research by Sarah Wells

Author's acknowledgements
The author would like to thank the *Share It!* team for all their support and encouragement.

The authors and publishers would like to thank the following for permission to reproduce their photographs:

Alamy Stock Photo/Classic Image p14, Alamy Stock Photo/Cultura RM p8(1);

Comstock p75(2);

Alamy Stock Photo/incamerastock p. 23(1b), Alamy Stock Photo/Tony Tallec p. 82(1.1);

Getty Images p. 44(2f), Getty Images/adventtr p. 55(2b), Getty Images/ALEAIMAGE p. 45(1b), Getty Images/Andy Crawford p. 42, Getty Images/Corbis/Lawrence Manning p. 75(2b), Getty Images/Digital Vision/Klaus Vedfelt p. 13(b), Getty Images/Digital Vision/Nick David p. 44(2d), Getty Images/Digital Vision/Ronnie Kaufman p. 44(2b), Getty Images/E+/Antagain p. 15(d), Getty Images/E+/BlackJack3D p. 35(2c), Getty Images/E+/DonNichols p. 55(2c table), Getty Images/E+/fcafotodigital p. 75(2c), Getty Images/E+/kali9 p. 73(2), Getty Images/E+/SDI Productions p. 82(1.2), Getty Images/E+/Vasko p. 75(2e), Getty Images/ElementalImaging p. 55(2e), Getty Images/EyeEm/Anfisa Kameneva p. 84(2d), Getty Images/EyeEm/Classen Rafael p. 55(2c), Getty Images/fizkes p. 45(2.1), Getty Images/Image Bank/Ariel Skelley p. 44(2e), Getty Images/Image Source p. 23(1c), Getty Images/iStock/abadonian p. 24(2c), Getty Images/iStock/Alexander Vorotyntsev p. 53(1b), Getty Images/iStock/bazilfoto p. 64(2c), Getty Images/iStock/BirdHunter591 p. 62(1.4), Getty Images/iStock/brunohaver p. 44(2c), Getty Images/iStock/burtonhill p. 64(2e), Getty Images/iStock/dragance137 p. 15(a), Getty Images/iStock/dragance137 p. 35(2a), Getty Images/iStock/Floortje p. 75(2d), Getty Images/iStock/gabes1976 p. 64(2f), Getty Images/iStock/GlobalP p. 64(2d), Getty Images/iStock/Jasonfang p. 84(2f), Getty Images/iStock/JeepFoto p. 22(1.3), Getty Images/iStock/kitthanes p. 23(1a), Getty Images/iStock/LAMBERTO JESUS p. 15(e), Getty Images/iStock/lom66 p. 35(2b), Getty Images/iStock/Mashot p. 15(b), Getty Images/iStock/Nataliia_Makarova p. 44(2a), Getty Images/iStock/Nerthuz p. 24(2e), Getty Images/iStock/rclassenlayouts p. 35(2d), Getty Images/iStock/scanrail p. 24(2a), Getty Images/iStock/subjug p. 35(2e), Getty Images/iStock/terrababy p. 22(1.1), Getty Images/iStock/TheSP4N1SH p. 35(2f), Getty Images/iStock/Witthaya Prasongsin p. 22(1.2), Getty Images/iStock/Zerbor p. 84(2a), Getty Images/iStockphoto/Coprid/Anton Starikov p. 23(1d), Getty Images/iStockphoto/DaddyBit,Valerii Kaliuzhnyi p. 64(2a), Getty Images/iStockphoto/globalIP p. 75(2f), Getty Images/iStockphoto/Ociacia p. 84(2c), Getty Images/iStockphoto/Scanrail p. 55(2a), Getty Images/Kazumasa Yanai p. 13(a), Getty Images/Maskot p. 45(1a), Getty Images/Moment/Vicki Smith p. 62(1.3), Getty Images/Moment/woottisak nirongboot p. 62(1.1), Getty Images/omgimages p. 45(1c), Getty Images/Photographer's Choice/Bernard Jaubert p. 15(c), Getty Images/Photographer's Choice/Steve Lewis Stock p. 22(1.4), Getty Images/Shingo Tosha/AFLO p. 13(c), Getty Images/Stephanie Rausser p. 45(2.2), Getty Images/The Image Bank/Dirk Anschutz p. 82(1.4), Getty Images/Valentin Wolf p. 62(1.2), Getty Images/Westend61 pp. 24(2d), 45(1d);

iStockphoto/Highwaystarz-Photography p. 84(2e), iStockphoto/hlphoto p. 75(2a), iStockphoto/scanrail p. 24(2b);

Macmillan Publishers Ltd p. 84(2b);

Shutterstock/chuchiko17 p. 53(1a), Shutterstock/Mariabo2015 p. 82(2.1), Shutterstock/Mariabo2015p p. 82(2.2), 82(2.3), 82(2.4), Shutterstock/Mirko Rosenau p. 64(2b), Shutterstock/New Africa p. 82(1.3), Shutterstock/Studio.G photography p. 53(1c), Shutterstock/Vilaiporn Chatchawal p. 73(1);

STOCKBYTE p. 55(2d);

STUDIO 8 p. 55(2f);

Ximena Cerón pp. 43, 63.

Printed and bound in Poland by CGS

2025 2024 2023 2022 2021
17 16 15 14 13 12 11 10 9 8